Milk

by Lynn Maslen Kertell
pictures by Sue Hendra

Scholastic Inc.
New York • Toronto • London • Auckland • Sydney • Mexico City • New Delhi • Hong Kong

Ask for Bob Books at your local bookstore, or visit www.bobbooks.com.

No part of this publication may be reproduced, stored in a retrieval system, or transmitted in any form, or by any means, electronic, mechanical, photocopying, recording, or otherwise, without written permission of the publisher. For information regarding permission, write to Scholastic Inc., Attention: Permissions Department, 557 Broadway, New York, NY 10012.

ISBN 978-0-545-34822-5

12 11 10 9 8 7 6 5 4 3 2 1   11 12 13 14 15/0

Printed in China / 68
This edition printing, January 2011

Mit had some milk in a jug.

The milk is not in a pan.

The milk is not in a tub.

Can Mit get some milk?

Mit can tip the jug.

Smack! Splat!

The milk did spill.
It is not in the jug.

Lap up some milk, Mit.

Mit had some milk to drink.

The
  End